SHORT ANTHEMS
FOR SMALL CHOIRS

Kevin Mayhew

We hope you enjoy *Short Anthems for Small Choirs*. Further copies are available from your local music shop or Christian bookshop.

In case of difficulty, please contact the publisher direct by writing to:

The Sales Department
KEVIN MAYHEW LTD
Buxhall
Stowmarket
Suffolk
IP14 3BW

Phone 01449 737978
Fax 01449 737834
E-mail info@kevinmayhewltd.com

Please ask for our complete catalogue of outstanding Church Music.

This compilation first published in Great Britain in 2000 by Kevin Mayhew Ltd.

ISBN 1 84003 581 1
ISMN M 57004 714 7
Catalogue No: 1450183

1 2 3 4 5 6 7 8 9

Cover design by Jonathan Stroulger
Music Setter: Rob Danter
Proof-reader: Adrian Vernon Fish

Printed and bound in Great Britain

Contents

Index of Uses

AVE VERUM CORPUS

Text: 14th century Latin
Music: Charles Gounod (1818-1893)
Edited by Andrew Gant

* *If sung unaccompanied, the first four bars should be hummed.*
If accompanied, the voices begin at bar 5.

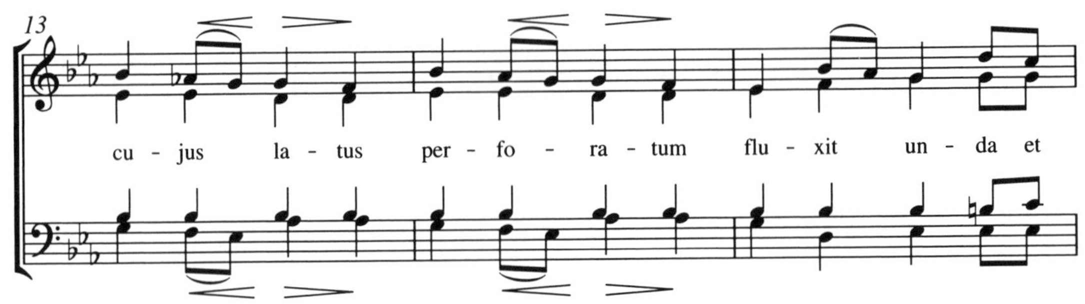
13
cu - jus la - tus per - fo - ra - tum flu - xit un - da et

16
p
cresc.
san - gui - ne, es - to no - bis præ - gus - ta - tum
p
cresc.

19
f
p
mor - tis in ex - a - mi - ne. O Je - su dul - cis,
f
p
O Je - su dul - cis, O

22
f
p
O Je - su pi - e, Je - su, Je - su fi - li Ma - ri - æ, in
Je - su pi - e,
f
p

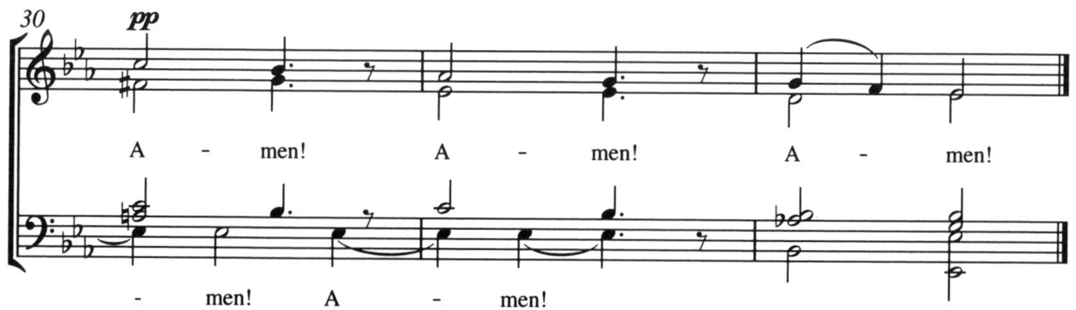

* *Top notes optional.*

Translation: Hail, true Body born of the Virgin Mary
which truly suffered and was sacrificed
on the cross for the human race;
from whose pierced side flowed water and blood,
be to us a foretatse in the crisis of death.
O dear Jesus, O holy Jesus,
Jesus, Jesus, son of Mary,
have mercy on us, have mercy on us,
O Jesus have mercy on us. Amen.

ADORAMUS TE, CHRISTE

Text: Unknown
Music: Théodore Dubois (1837-1924)
Edited by David Patrick

Translation: We adore you, O Christ, and we bless you,
who on your holy cross suffered for the redemption of the world.

AVE MARIA

Text: Luke 1
Music: Jacob Arcadelt (1505-1568)

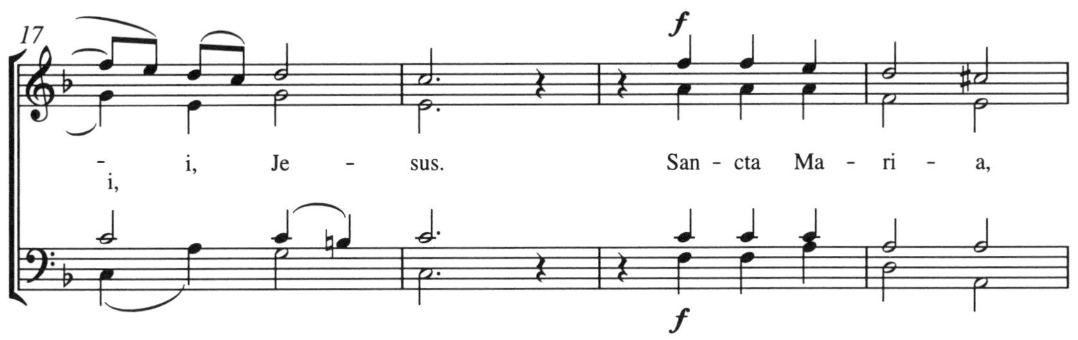

Translation: Hail Mary, full of grace, the Lord is with thee, hail Mary:
Blessed art thou, blessed art thou among women,
And blessed is the fruit of thy womb, Jesus.
Holy Mary, pray, pray for us. Amen.

HERE IS BREAD

Text: Graham Kendrick (b.1950)
Music: Graham Kendrick, arr. Christopher Tambling

14
here is peace,
Christ is with us,
he is with us;
know his grace,
18
S
A
In this bread
T
B
find his peace,
feast on Je - sus
here.
In this
(With Ped.)
22
there is heal - ing,
in this cup
is life for e - ver.
In this mo - ment,
bread there is heal - ing,
life for e - ver.
In this

26
by the Spi - rit Christ is with us here.
mo - ment Christ is with us here.

Full Choir
29
Here we are, joined in one, Christ is with us,

32
he is with us; we'll pro- claim till he comes

35
Je - sus cru - ci - fied.
S
A
In this bread
T
B
In this
38
there is heal - ing, in this cup is life for e - ver.
bread there is heal - ing, life for e - ver.
41
rall.
In this mo - ment, by the Spi - rit, Christ is with us here.
In this mo - ment Christ is with us here.
rall.

GOD BE IN MY HEAD

Text: from 'The Book of Hours' (1514)
Music: Malcolm Archer (b.1952)

Sopranos and Altos
mf (repeat p)
God be in my mouth, and in my speak - ing;
God be in my heart, and in my think - ing;
Slower
mf
God be at mine end,
and
p
at my de - part - ing.
dim.
pp
Ah.
S A
T B
Ped.

BREAD OF HEAVEN, ON THEE WE FEED

Text: Josiah Conder (1789-1855)
Music: Richard Lloyd (b.1933)

17
this blest cup of sa - cri - fice; 'tis thy wounds our heal - ing give,
21
mf
to thy Cross we look and live: thou our life! O let us be
25
rall.
meno mosso
pp
rall.
root - ed, graft - ed, built in thee, root - ed, graft - ed, built in thee.
mf
pp

CHRIST BE WITH ME

Text: ascribed to St. Patrick, trans. Cecil Frances Alexander (1818-1895)
Music: Canon in D (Johann Pachelbel 1653-1706)
arranged by Noel Rawsthorne

13
S
A
p
Christ be with me, Christ with - in me, Christ be-hind me, Christ be-fore me,
T
B
p
Solo
p
Sw.
17
cresc.
dim.
Christ be - side me, Christ to guide me, Christ to com-fort and re - store me.
cresc.
dim.
cresc.
dim.
21
p
25
Tenor Solo (or Full)
p
Christ be - neath me, Christ a - bove me, Christ in qui - et, Christ in dan - ger,
Sw.
p

29
cresc.
dim.
Christ in hearts of all that love me, Christ in care of friend and stran - ger.
cresc.
dim.
33
S
A
p
Christ be - neath me, Christ a - bove me, Christ in qui - et, Christ in dan - ger,
T
B
p
Solo
p
Sw.
37
cresc.
rall. e dim.
p
Christ in hearts of all that love me, Christ in care of friend and stran - ger.
rall. e dim.
p
cresc.
rall. e dim.
p

O KING, AND DESIRE OF ALL NATIONS

Text: from the Latin *O Antiphon*
Music: John Stainer (1840-1901)

18
p
pp
cresc.
come and save man, whom thou form - edst from the clay, come and save
23
f
man, whom thou form - edst from the clay, come and save man, whom thou
28
form - edst from the clay, come, Lord Je - sus, come!
Man.

34
p
Come, Lord Je - sus, come! Come, Lord
p
40
pp
Je - sus, come! Come, Lord Je - sus,
pp
pp
ppp
Ped.
47
rall.
ppp
come!
rall.
ppp

I WILL SING OF THE LORD

Text: Psalm 13:6
Music: Jeremiah Clarke (c.1674-1707)
Edited by David Patrick

17
f
cause he hath dealt so lov - ing-ly with me: yea, I will
f
f
22
praise the name of the Lord, will praise the name of the Lord most
28
rall.
high - est, will praise the name of the Lord most high - est.
rall.

SING, HOLY SPIRIT, SING!

Text: Michael Forster (b.1946)
Music: Rosalie Bonighton (b.1946)

13
Rise, Ho-ly Spi-rit, rise! Beck-on the dawn of the new cre-a-tion,
Rise, Ho-ly Spi-rit, rise! Beck-on the dawn of the new cre-a-tion,

17
rit. last time only
Fine
call - ing all the world in the lan - guage of love.
rit. last time only
call - ing all the world to life in the lan - guage of love.
(last time)
Fine
rit. last time only

21
1.
S A
1. Where there is dark - ness, fear and sor-row, be the sign of a
T B

24
new to - mor - row; keep the light of hope e - ver glow - ing,
27
D.S.
foun - tains of jus - tice and right - eous - ness flow - ing.
30
2.
2. Spi - rit of God, with - in us liv - ing, life in all its a -
33
bun - dance giv - ing, let our lives be signs of your glo - ry,
36
D.S.
give us a part in your won - der - ful sto - ry.

For Jaymi Candide Bandtock

HERE, O MY LORD

Text: Horatius Bonar (1808-1889)
Music: Alan Viner (b.1951)

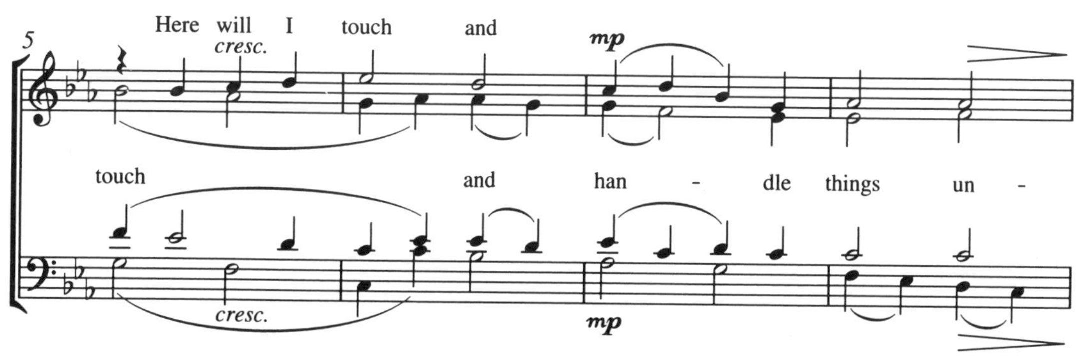

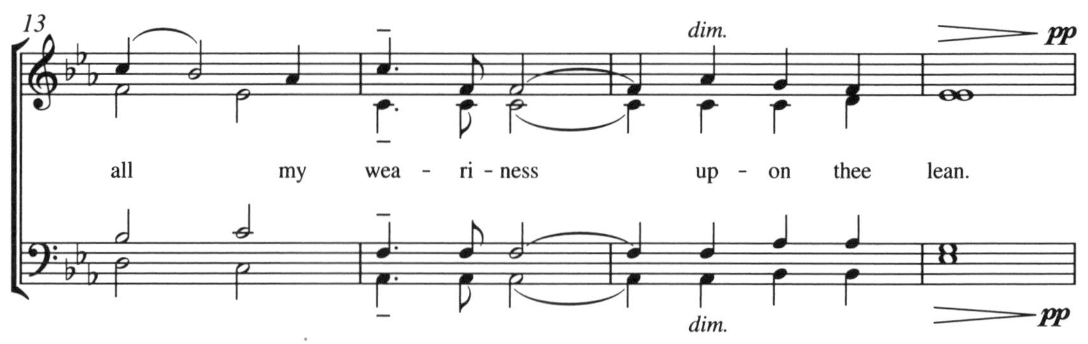
13
dim.
pp
all my wea - ri - ness up - on thee lean.
dim.
pp

Poco più mosso
17
mf
cresc.
Here would I feed up - on the bread of God, here drink with
mf
cresc.

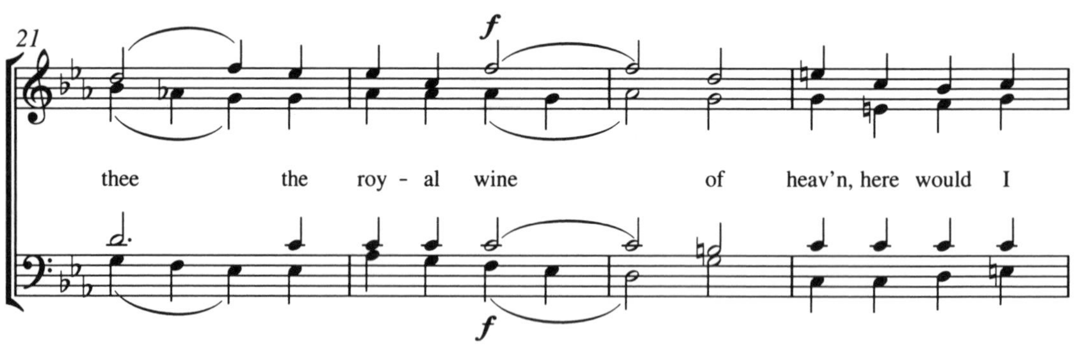
21
f
thee the roy - al wine of heav'n, here would I
f

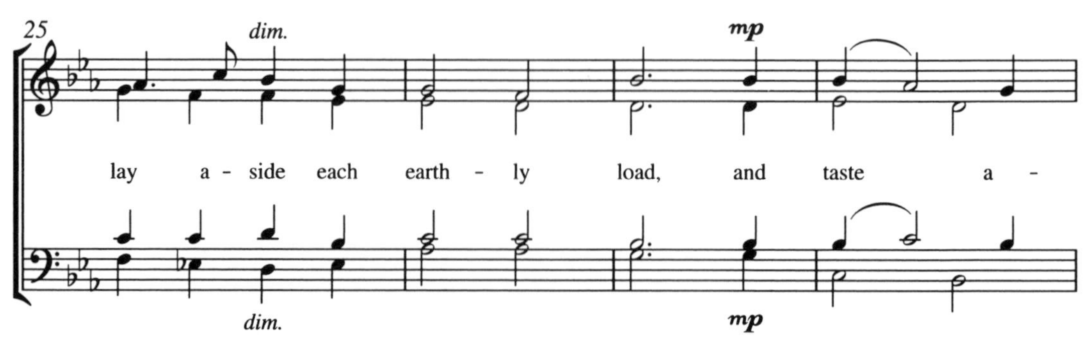
25
dim.
mp
lay a - side each earth - ly load, and taste a -
dim.
mp

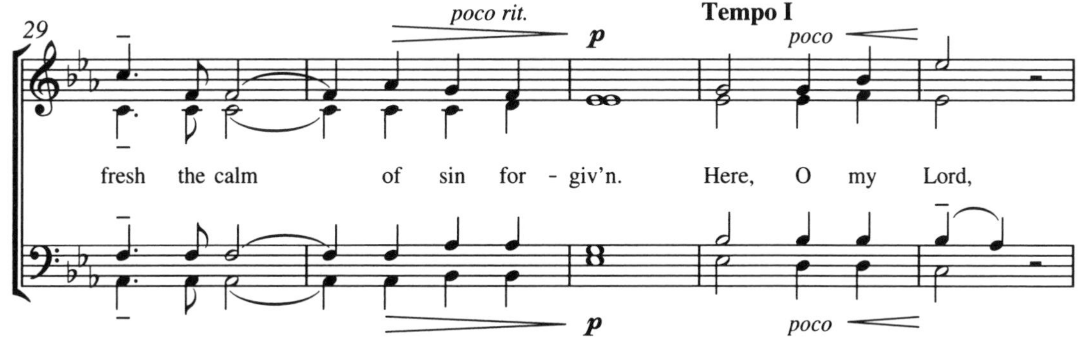
29
poco rit.
Tempo I
p
poco
fresh the calm of sin for - giv'n. Here, O my Lord,
p
poco

34
poco dim. e rall.
a niente
p
here, O my Lord, I see thee face to face.
p
a niente

COME, DEAREST LORD

Text: Isaac Watts (1674-1748)
Music: Richard Lloyd (b.1933)

14
mf
Come, fill our hearts with in - ward strength, make
mf
hearts with
17
mp
our en - lar - ged souls pos - sess and learn the
mp
20
height and breadth and length of
23
mf
rall.
mp
thine un - mea - su - ra - ble grace.
mf
mp
Meno mosso
27
A - men, a - men.
pp
A - men, a - men.
A - men, a - men.
pp

COME, HOLY GHOST

Text: based on 'Veni Creator Spiritus': Vs. 1-3 John Cosin (1594-1672);
Vs. 4, 5: Michael Forster (b. 1946)
Music: Vs. 1, 3 and 5: Plainsong arr. Colin Mawby (b. 1936);
Vs. 2, 4: George Malcolm (b.1917)

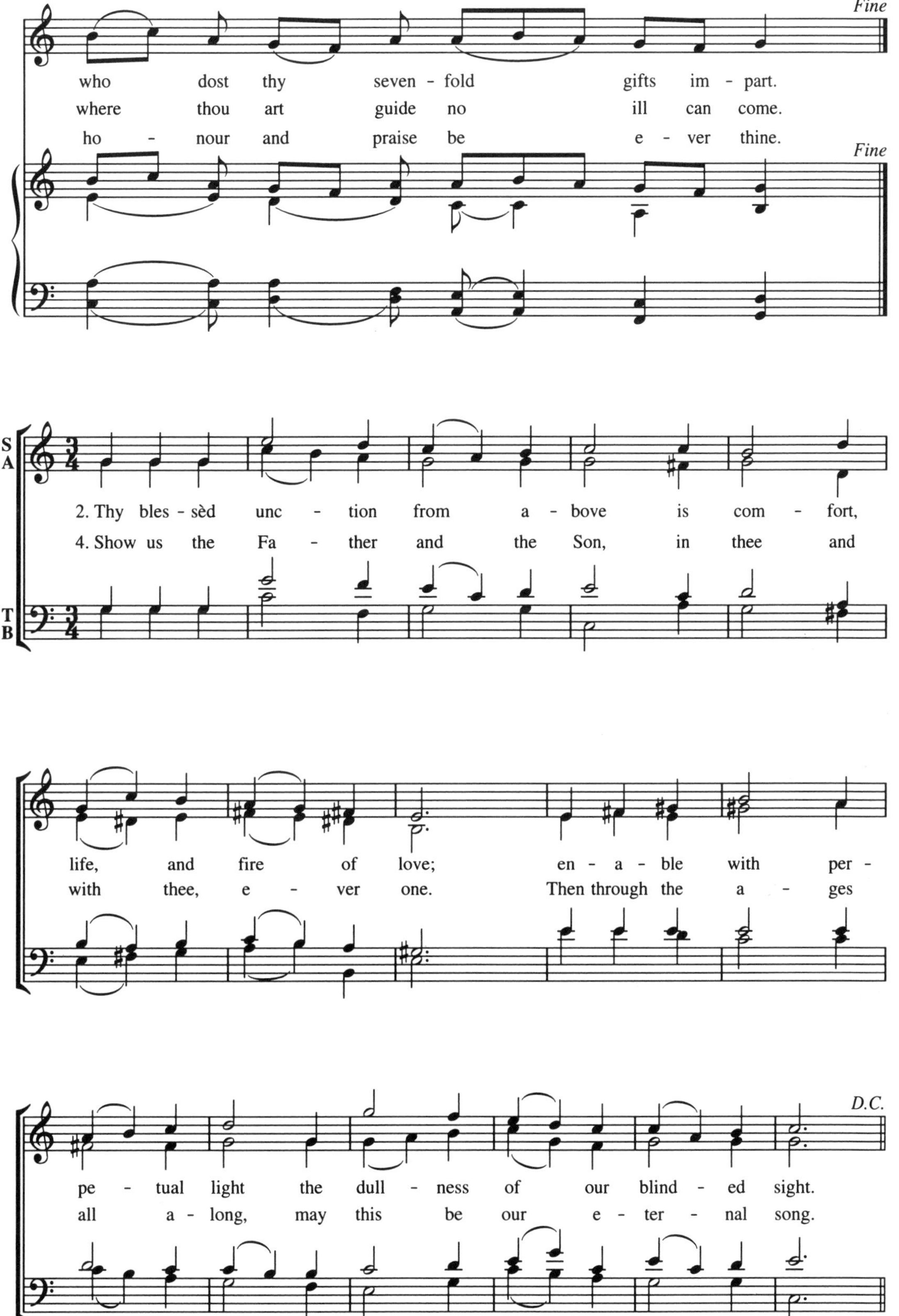

Fine
who dost thy seven - fold gifts im - part.
where thou art guide no ill can come.
ho - nour and praise be e - ver thine.
Fine
S
A
T
B
2. Thy bles - sèd unc - tion from a - bove is com - fort,
4. Show us the Fa - ther and the Son, in thee and
life, and fire of love; en - a - ble with per -
with thee, e - ver one. Then through the a - ges
pe - tual light the dull - ness of our blind - ed sight.
all a - long, may this be our e - ter - nal song.
D.C.

TIMELESS LOVE

Text: Timothy Dudley-Smith (b.1926) based on Psalm 89
Music: Norman Warren (b.1934)

12
glo - ry, love more firm than an- cient earth. Tell his faith - ful-ness a -
found - ed, skies and seas de-clare his name. Wind and storm o - bey his
16
f
broad, who is like him, praise the Lord!
word,
f
Sw.
LH
mp
20
cresc.

24
All voices in Unison
f
3. Truth and righ - teous - ness en - throne him, just and
27
e - qual are his ways; more than hap - py those who
30
own him, more than joy their songs of praise! Sun and shield and great re -
rall. al fine
34
S A
T B
ward – who is like him, praise the Lord!
ff

For the Choir of All Saints', Friern Barnet, London

JESU, JOYAUNCE OF MY HEART

Text: Johann Flitner (1618-1678), trans. G.R. Woodward
Music: melody by Johann Rudolph Ahle (1625-1673),
harmonised by J.S. Bach (1685-1750)
Edited by David Patrick

11
Full
Solo
Full
ho - ly Je - su; sure de-fence from Sa - tan's dart, sweet-est Je -
Ped.
Man.
Ped.
16
su; Je - su, sweet-est Je - su.
mp
21
Solo
mp
Full
Thou-sand times I think of thee, my Re-deem - er; on - ly yearn thy
Man.
Ped.
Man.

26
Full
Solo
mf
face to see, my Re - deem - er; long-ing for thy com - pa-ny,
mf
Ped.
Man.

31
Full
poco rall.
my Re-deem - er; Je - su my Re - deem - er.
poco rall.
Ped.

HIDE NOT THOU THY FACE

Text: Psalm 27:10
Music: Richard Farrant (d.1581)

18
li - ver us from all our sins, for thy mer - cy's sake, for thy mer- cy's

22
poco rall.
sake de - li - ver us from all our sins, de - li - ver us from all our sins.

LAUDATE DOMINUM

Text: Psalm 150
Music: Giuseppe Ottavio Pitoni (1657-1743)

16
lau - da - te e - um
e - um in vir - tu - ti-bus e - jus:
lau - da-te e - um
se - cun - dum
lau - da - te e - um

21
mul- ti - tu - di - nem mag-ni-tu - di-nis e - jus. Lau-da - te, lau-da-te

26
e - um in so - no tu - bae, in so - no tu -

31
bae: lau - da - te e - um in psal - te - ri - o et ci - tha-ra.

36
Lau - da - te e - um
Lau - da - te e - um in cym - ba - lis be - ne so - nan - ti - bus:

40
laud - det Do - mi - num.
lau - det Do - mi - num.
o - mnis spi - ri - tus
lau - det Do - mi - num.

Slow and broad
45
Al - le - lu - ia, al - le - lu - ia, al - le - lu - ia, al - le -

50
lu - ia, al - le - lu - ia, al - le - lu - ia.

LET THY BLOOD IN MERCY POURED

Text: from John Brownlie (1859-1925)
Music: Stanley Vann (b.1910)

AVE VERUM CORPUS

Text: 14th Century
Music: Wolfgang Amadeus Mozart (1756-1791)

13
f
im - mo - la - tum in cru - ce pro ho - mi - ne.
f
im - mo - la - tum in cru - ce pro ho - mi - ne.
f
im - mo - la - tum in cru - ce pro ho - mi - ne.
f
im-mo - la - tum in cru - ce pro ho - mi - ne.
f
19
p cresc.
Cu - jus la - tus per - fo -
p cresc.
Cu - jus la - tus per - fo -
p cresc.
Cu - jus la - tus per - fo -
p cresc.
Cu - jus la - tus per - fo -
dim.
p cresc.
Man.

25
dim.
p
ratum unda fluxit et sanguine;
dim.
p
ratum unda fluxit et sanguine;
dim.
ratum unda fluxit et sanguine;
dim.
ratum unda fluxit et sanguine;
dim.
p
30
pp
cresc.
esto nobis prægustatum in mor-
pp
cresc.
esto nobis prægustatum in mor-
pp
cresc.
esto nobis prægustatum in
pp
cresc.
esto nobis prægustatum in
pp
cresc.

Translation: Hail, hail true Body born of the Virgin Mary which truly suffered and was sacrificed on the cross for the human race, from whose pierced side flowed water and blood. Be to us a foretaste in the crisis of death, in the crisis of death.

BLEST ARE YOU, O GOD, CREATOR

Text: Michael Forster (b.1946)
Music: June Nixon

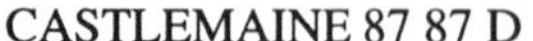

CASTLEMAINE 87 87 D

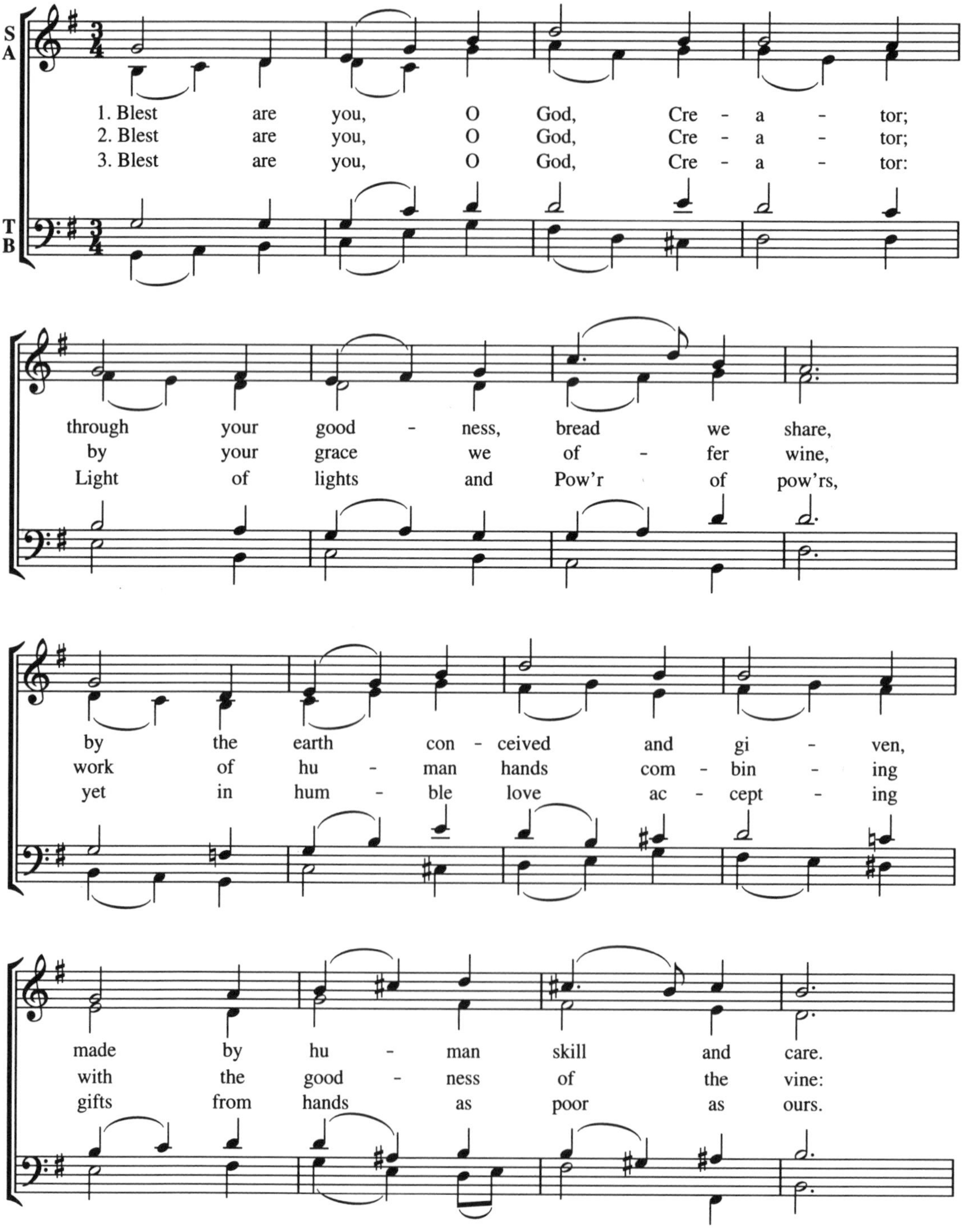
S
A
T
B
1. Blest are you, O God, Cre - a - tor;
2. Blest are you, O God, Cre - a - tor;
3. Blest are you, O God, Cre - a - tor:
through your good - ness, bread we share,
by your grace we of - fer wine,
Light of lights and Pow'r of pow'rs,
by the earth con - ceived and gi - ven,
work of hu - man hands com - bin - ing
yet in hum - ble love ac - cept - ing
made by hu - man skill and care.
with the good - ness of the vine:
gifts from hands as poor as ours.

Com - mon food, by grace made ho - ly,
cup of bles - sing and of sor - row,
Love it - self our love de - sir - ing,
bread of life to us will be.
love's re - deem - ing a - go - ny,
O what awe - some Mys - te - ry!
Share we in the feast of hea - ven;
poured for us, our souls re - fresh - ing;
In our giv - ing and re - ceiv - ing,
blest be God e - ter - nal - ly!
blest be God e - ter - nal - ly!
blest be God e - ter - nal - ly!

FATHER GOD, WE WORSHIP YOU

Text: Graham Kendrick (b.1950)
Music: Graham Kendrick, arr. Christopher Tambling

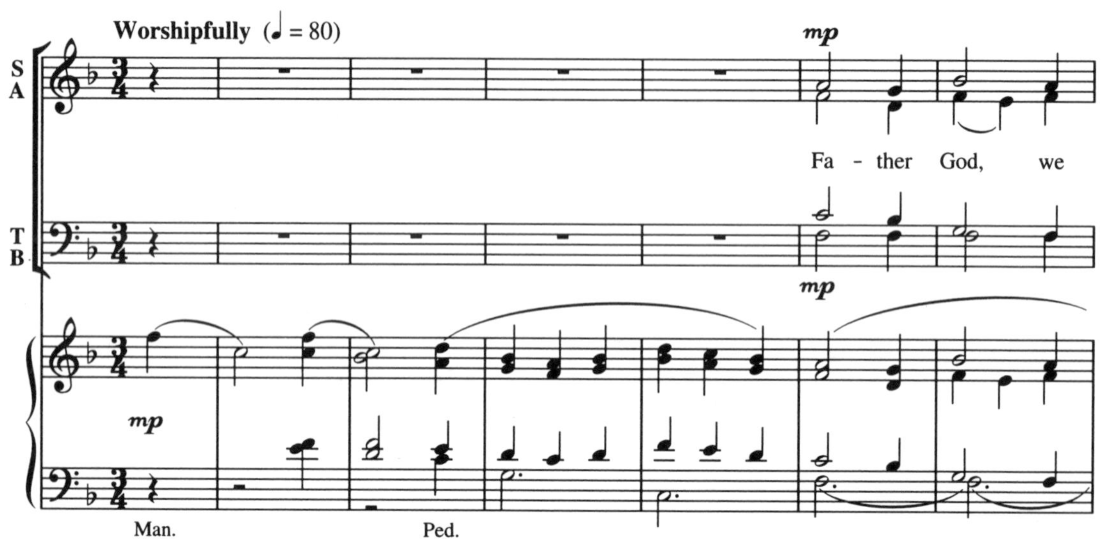

13
As you move a - mong us now, we wor -
18
ship you.
Tenors and Basses mf
Je - sus King, we
mf
25
T
B
wor - ship you, help us lis - ten now to you.

31
Sopranos and Altos
As you move a - mong us now, we wor - ship you.
38
S
A
f
Spi - rit pure, we wor - ship
T
B
f
f
44
you, with your fire our zeal re - new.

49
allargando
As you move a - mong us now, we wor -
allargando
54
ship
- ship you.
ship
ff

LORD, I LIFT MY HANDS TO YOU

Text: Nick Fawcett (b.1957)
Music: Adagio from Pathétique Sonata (Ludwig van Beethoven 1770-1827)
arranged by Noel Rawsthorne

7
tur - moil, heart crushed by care.
Gt.
3

10
Tenors
p
Come to me and find rest for your soul. Don't
Gt.
p
Sw.

14
wor - ry, simp-ly trust me, my love can make you

17
Poco meno mosso
S
A
T
B
whole. Lord, I come, the
3
simile
20
storm with - in now stilled, peace flows
23
through me, your word ful - filled.
rall.

WE COME IN FAITH TO MEET OUR LORD

Text: Anonymous
Music: Traditional American, arr. Stanley Vann (b.1910)

GOD IS A SPIRIT

Text: John 4:24
Music: Henry Smart (1813-1879)

18
must wor - ship
spi - rit wor - ship him in spi-rit and in truth:
23
p
for the Fa - ther seek-eth such to wor - ship him,
p for the Fa - ther
28
mp f
for the Fa - ther seek - eth such, seek - eth
mp f
33
dim.
such to wor - ship him.
dim.
38
p
God is a Spi - rit.
p

LEAD ME, LORD

Text: Psalm 5:8; 4:9
Music: Samuel Sebastian Wesley (1810-1876) arr. Colin Hand

17
make thy way plain be - fore my face.
make thy way plain be - fore my face.
make thy way plain be - fore my face.
make thy way plain be - fore my face.
Man.
21
Soprano Solo
For it is thou, Lord, thou, Lord, on - ly, that
25
cresc.
mp
p
mak - est me dwell in safe - ty.
cresc.
mp
p
Ped.

29
All Sopranos
p
For it is thou, Lord, thou, Lord, on - ly, that
For it is thou, Lord, thou, Lord, on - ly, that
For it is thou, Lord, thou, Lord, on - ly, that
For it is thou, Lord, thou, Lord, on - ly, that
33
cresc.
mp
p
rit.
ma - kest me dwell in safe - ty.
ma - kest me dwell in safe - ty.
ma - kest me dwell in safe - ty.
ma - kest me dwell in safe - ty.

THE KING IS AMONG US

Text: Graham Kendrick (b.1950)
Music: Graham Kendrick, arr. Christopher Tambling

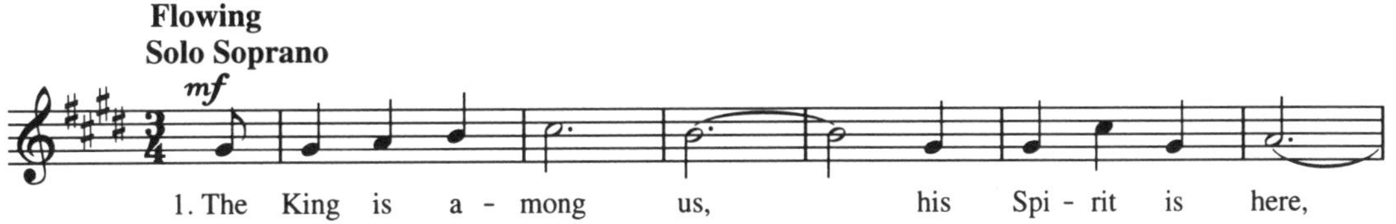

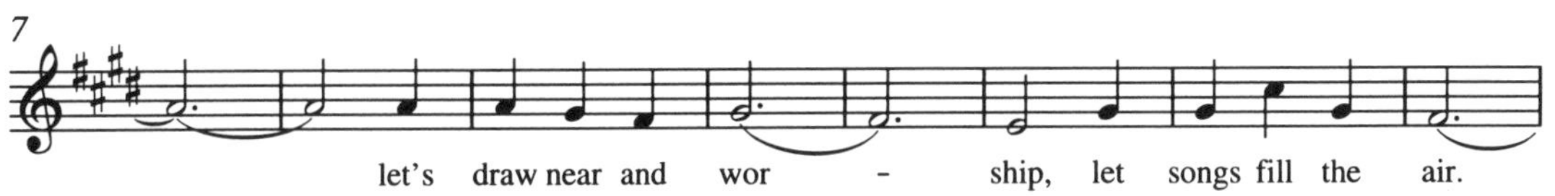

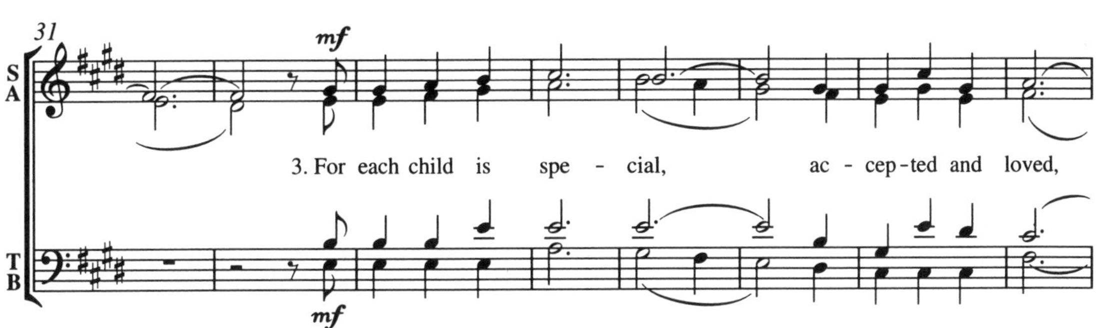

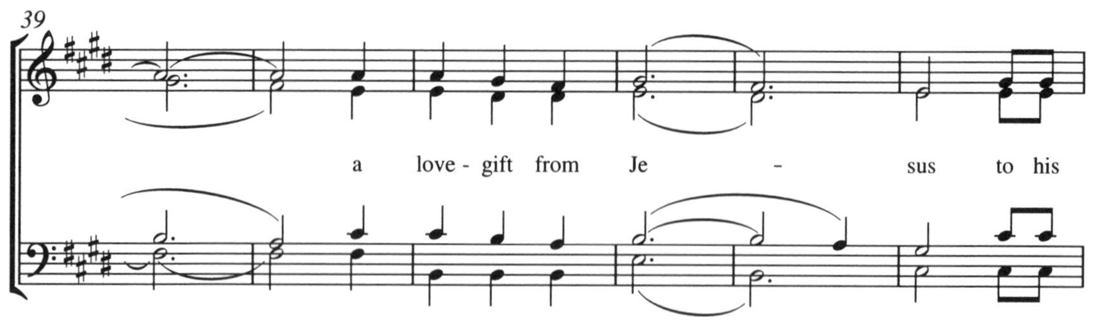
39
a love - gift from Je - sus to his

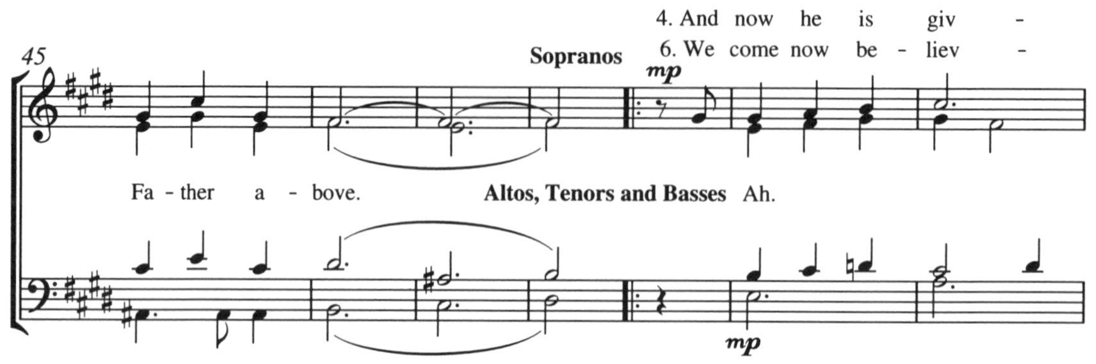
45
4. And now he is giv -
Sopranos
6. We come now be - liev -
mp
Fa - ther a - bove.
Altos, Tenors and Basses Ah.
mp

ing his gifts to us all for
51
ing your pro - mise of pow'r for

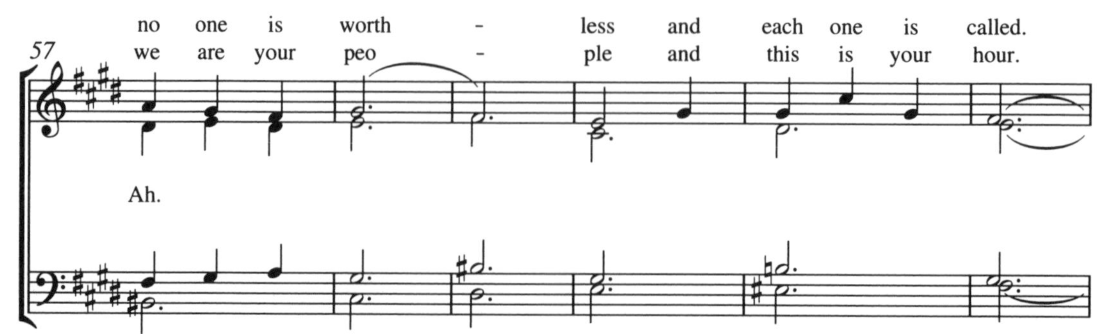
no one is worth - less and each one is called.
57
we are your peo - ple and this is your hour.
Ah.

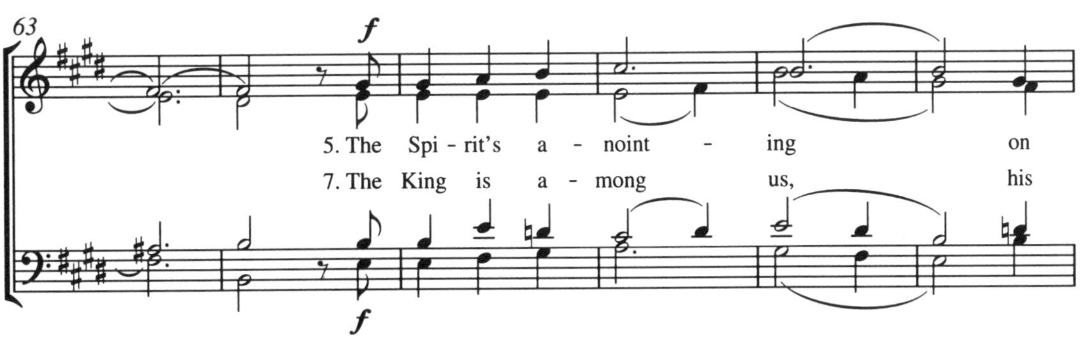
63
f
5. The Spi - rit's a - noint - ing on
7. The King is a - mong us, his
f

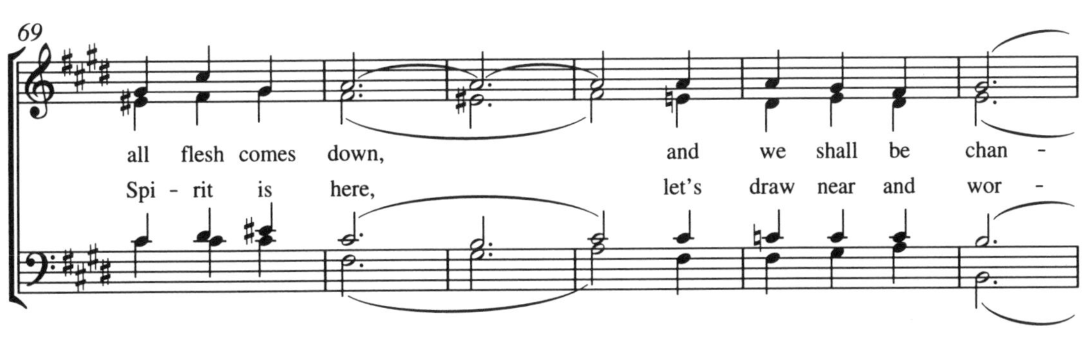
69
all flesh comes down, and we shall be chan -
Spi - rit is here, let's draw near and wor -

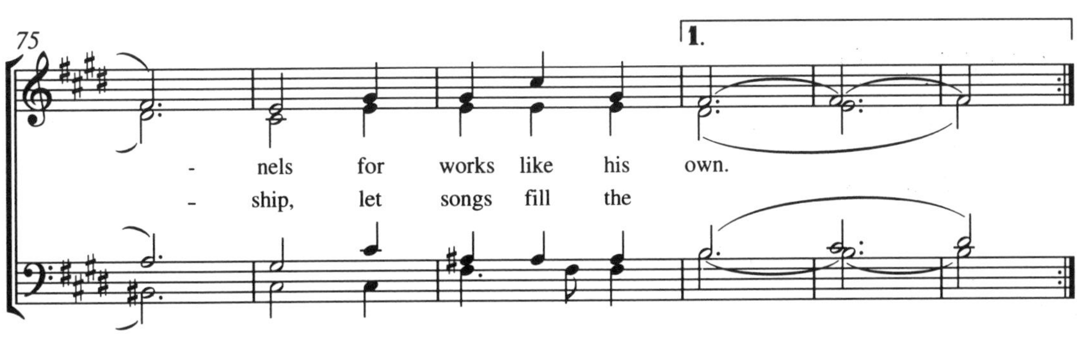
75
1.
- nels for works like his own.
- ship, let songs fill the

81
2.
rit.
air, let songs fill the air.

GOD TO ENFOLD ME

Text: Traditional Celtic Prayer
Music: Stanley Vann (b.1910)

13
a tempo
mp
God in my suf - fic - ing, God in my slum - ber,
mp
15
rall.
Slower
p
ppp
God in my e - ver liv - ing soul, God in mine e - ter - ni - ty.
p
ppp

HOSANNA TO THE SON OF DAVID

Text: Matthew 21:9
Music: Noel Rawsthorne (b.1929)

18
Bles - sed
mp
name of the Lord. Bles - sed is he who
mp

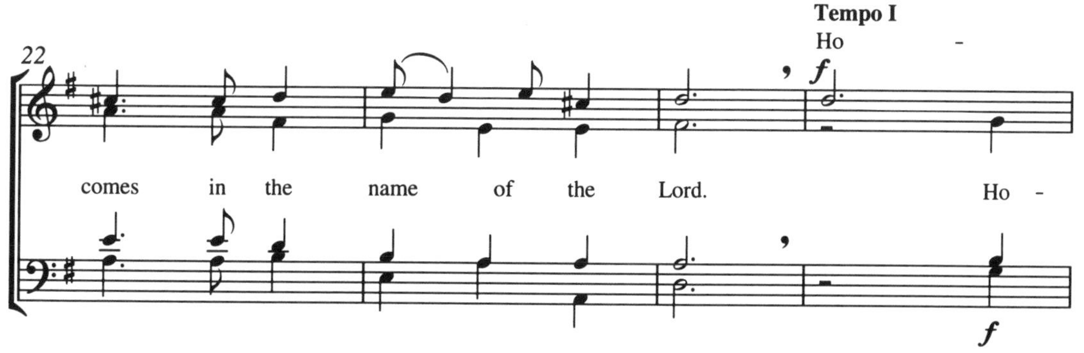
22
Tempo I
Ho -
f
comes in the name of the Lord. Ho -
f

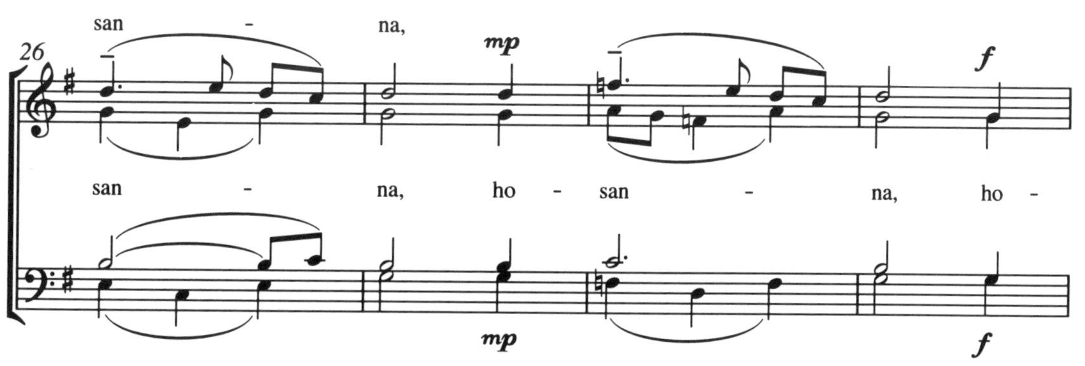
26
san - na,
mp
f
san - na, ho - san - na, ho -
mp
f

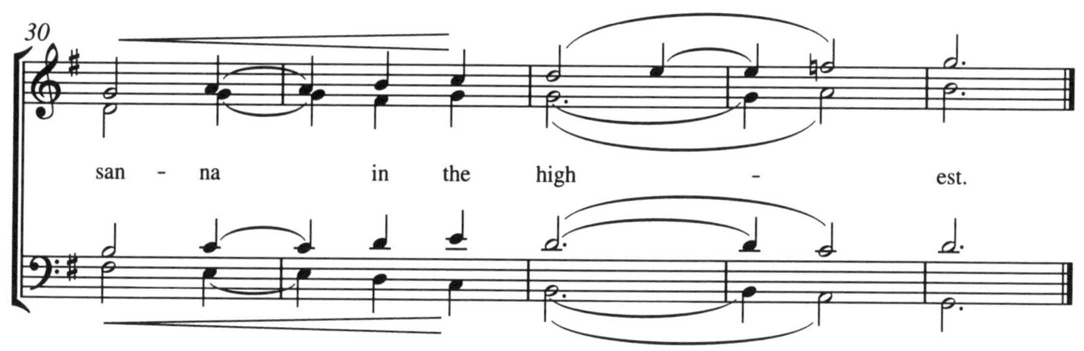
30
san - na in the high - est.

O COME AND MOURN WITH ME

Text: Frederick William Faber (1814-1863)
Music: Michael Higgins (b.1981)

COME WITH US, O BLESSED JESUS

Text: J. H. Hopkins (1820-1891)
Music: Stanley Vann (b.1910)

JESUS CHRIST IS RIS'N TODAY

Text: from 'Lyra Davidica' (1708)
Music: Richard Lloyd (b.1933)

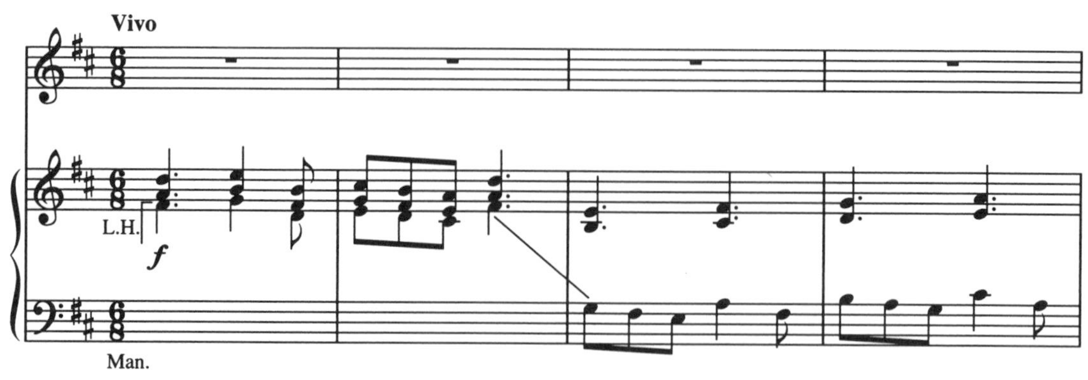

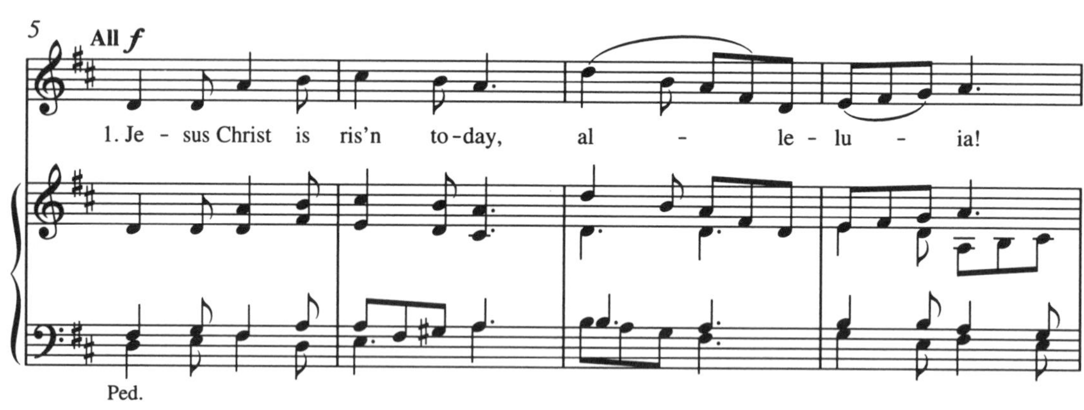

13
Who did once, up - on the cross, al - le - lu - ia!
17
Suf - fer to re - deem our loss, al - le - lu - ia!
21
mf
S
A
2. Hymns of praise then let us sing, al - le - lu - ia!
T
B
mf
25
Un - to Christ, our heav'n - ly king, al - le - lu - ia!

29
cresc.
Who en- dured the cross and grave, al - le - lu - ia!
cresc.
33
f
Sin - ners to re - deem and save, al - le - lu - ia!
f
37
poco allarg.
L.H.
f
Man.
Poco meno mosso
Descant
41
f
Al - le - lu - ia! Al - le - lu - ia!
All other voices
f
3. But the pains which he en- dured, al - le - lu - ia!
f
Ped.

45
Our sal - va - tion, al - le - lu - ia!
Our sal - va - tion hath pro - cured; al - le - lu - ia!
49
Now he's king, al - le - lu - ia!
Now a - bove the sky he's king, al - le - lu - ia!
53
allarg.
molto rall.
Where the an - gels e - ver sing, al - le - lu - ia!
Where the an - gels e - ver sing, al - le - lu - ia!
allarg.
molto rall.

O PRAISE GOD IN HIS HOLINESS

Text: Psalm 150
Music: John Weldon (1676-1736)
Edited by David Patrick

11
no - ble acts, praise him ac - cord - ing to his ex - cel-lent great - ness.
16
mf
Praise him in the sound of the trum - pet, praise him up - on the
sound of the
mf
mf
21
f
lute and harp. Praise him in the cym - bals and dan - ces,
f
f

26
praise him up - on the strings and pipe. Let ev - 'ry-thing
31
ff
that hath breath praise the Lord, let ev - 'ry-thing
ff
ff
36
molto rall.
that hath breath praise the Lord.
molto rall.

DAY BY DAY

Text: St Richard of Chichester
Music: Norman Warren (b.1934)

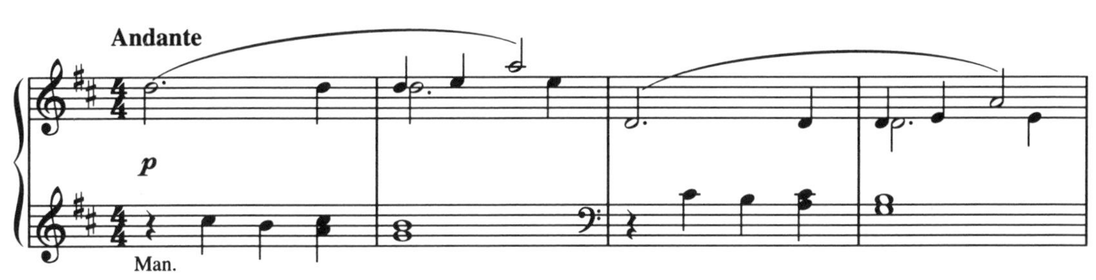

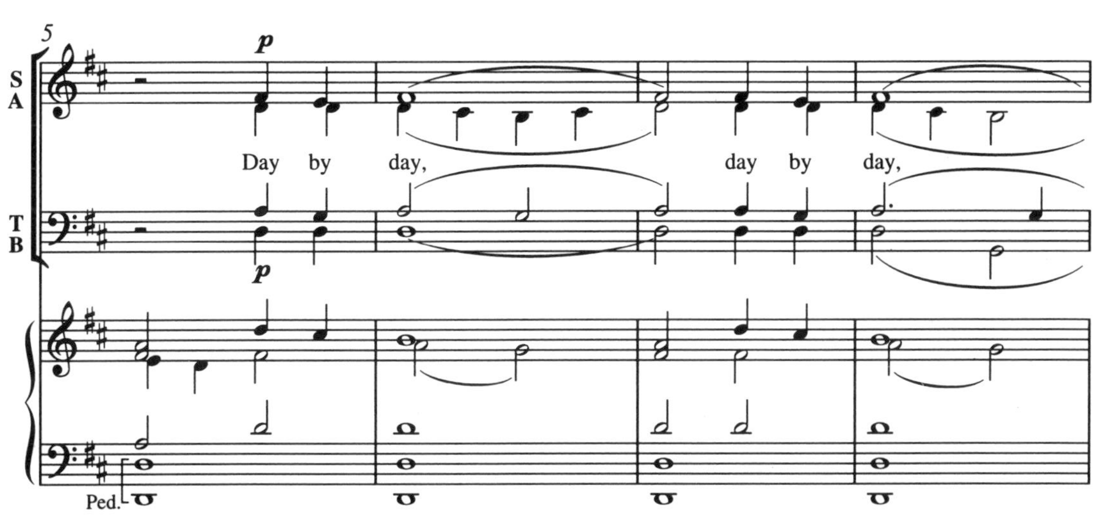

13
mf
to see you more clear - ly, to love you more
mf
mf
17
dear - ly, to fol - low you more near - ly, day by
21
f
day. To see you more clear - ly, to love you more
f
f

25
dim.
dear - ly, to fol - low you more near - ly day by
dim.
dim.
29
p
day, day by day.
p
L.H.
p

O MAY MY SOUL ON THEE REPOSE

Text: Thomas Ken (1637-1711)
Music: Alan Ridout (1934-1996)

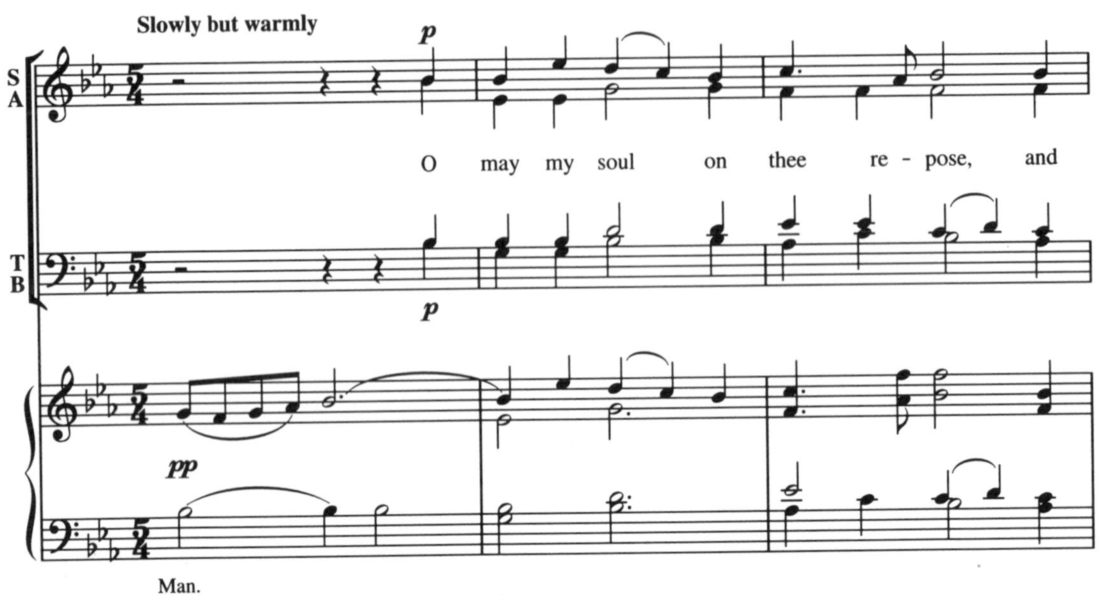

7
vi - go - rous make to serve my God when I a - wake. Praise
Ped.
10
God, from whom all bles - sings flow; praise him, all crea - tures
13
here be - low; praise him a - bove, ye hea - ven - ly hosts; praise

16
Fa - ther, Son, and Ho - ly Ghost.

DRAW NIGH AND TAKE THE BODY OF THE LORD

Text: 7th century Latin, trans. J. Neale
Music: Robert Jones (b.1945)

SEEK THE LORD

Text: Isaiah 55:6
Music: Harrison Oxley

12
call up - on him
mf cresc.
f
Lord while he may be found: call, call up - on
f
mf cresc.
f
mf
cresc.
f
17
mf
p call up - on him
p
him while he is near, call, call up - on
p
call up - on him, up - on
p
mf
p
mf
22
dim.
while he is near.
pp
mf
him while he is near.
mf
dim.
pp
(Sw.)
dim.
pp
Ped.

IN AN UPPER ROOM

Text: Nick Fawcett (b.1957)
Music: Prelude in C minor (Frédéric Chopin 1810-1849)
arranged by Noel Rawsthorne

7
dim.
p
ho - ver like a cloud o - ver ev - 'ry-thing. Haunt - ed fa - ces
how could God al - low his own Son to die? Then a voice breaks
put your hand in mine, for I long to bless. Take this cup, my
dim.
p
dim.
p
Man.
10
rall. e dim.
pp
chok - ing back the tears, eyes once full of hope tor - tured now by fears.
gent - ly through their pain, Je - sus, with a smile, speaks his word a - gain.
blood poured out for you, through this sac - ri - fice, life be - gins a - new.
rall. e dim.
pp
rall. e dim.
pp
Ped.

MORNING HAS BROKEN

Text: Eleanor Farjeon (1881-1965)
Music: Traditional Gaelic melody, arr. Christopher Tambling

18
Descant
Ah,
All, unison
3. Mine is the sun - light! Mine is the morn - ing born of the
Ped.
20
ah,
one light E - den saw play! Praise with e - la - tion, praise ev - 'ry
ah,
23
ah.
morn - ing, God's re - cre - a - tion of the new day!

PROCLAIM THE STORY

Text: Nick Fawcett (b.1957)
Music: Te Deum Prelude (Marc-Antoine Charpentier 1636-1704)
arranged by Noel Rawsthorne

7
known to all his glo - ry, lift up his name on high!
11
14
18
mf
He comes to reign for e - ver-more, come
mf
mf

21
kneel, a - dore, bow down in awe; lift up your hearts and
24
wor - ship Christ, whom God has crowned as Lord!
27
31

Broader
34
unis. f
Sing out, sing out ho - san - na! Re -
unis. f
f
37
div.
joice and greet the King of kings! Lift high his roy - al
div.
40
rall.
ban - ner, lift up your voice and sing.
rall.

DEEP WITHIN ME

Text: Hugh Dickinson (b.1929)
Music: Michael Higgins (b.1981)

13
16
mp
S
Stand be-fore me, liv-ing Lord. Let me see in Je-sus'
T
mp
mp
19
face the love of your in-car-nate Word, foun-tain,
22
spring and well of grace.

25
S
A
T
B
mp
Clothe me in your Spi-rit's
mp
mp
28
love;
let your shi-ning ne-ver cease;
31
Meno mosso
p
rall.
pp
let my spi-rit al-ways move in the ra - di-ance of peace.
p
pp

INCLINE THINE EAR

Text: Psalm 31:2
Music: Friedrich Heinrich Himmel (1765-1814)

10

Lord, make haste to de - li - ver me, in - cline thine

Lord, make haste to de - li - ver me, in - cline thine

O Lord, make haste to de - li - ver me, in - cline thine

O Lord, make haste to de - li - ver me, in - cline thine

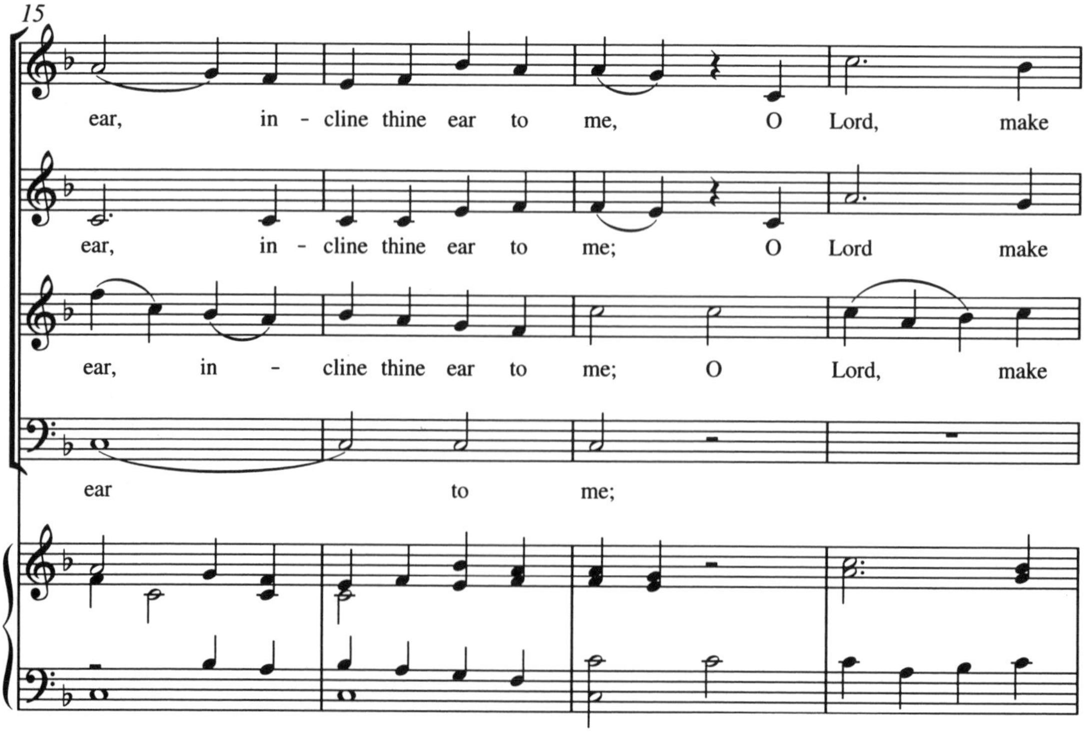

15

ear, in - cline thine ear to me, O Lord, make

ear, in - cline thine ear to me; O Lord make

ear, in - cline thine ear to me; O Lord, make

ear to me;

19

haste, make haste to de - li - ver me, O save me for thy

haste, make haste to de - li - ver me, O save me for thy

haste make haste to de - li - ver me, O save me for thy

O Lord, save

23

mer-cy's sake, O save me, save me for thy mer - cy's sake.

mer-cy's sake, O save me, save me for thy mer - cy's sake.

mer-cy's sake, O save me, save me for thy mer - cy's sake.

me, O save me, save me for thy mer - cy's sake.

For Susie and Robin

THE GRACE OF CHRIST

Text: John Newton (1725-1807)
Music: Richard Lloyd (b.1933)

SHEPHERD OF SOULS

Text: James Montgomery (1771-1854)
Music: Stanley Vann (b.1910)

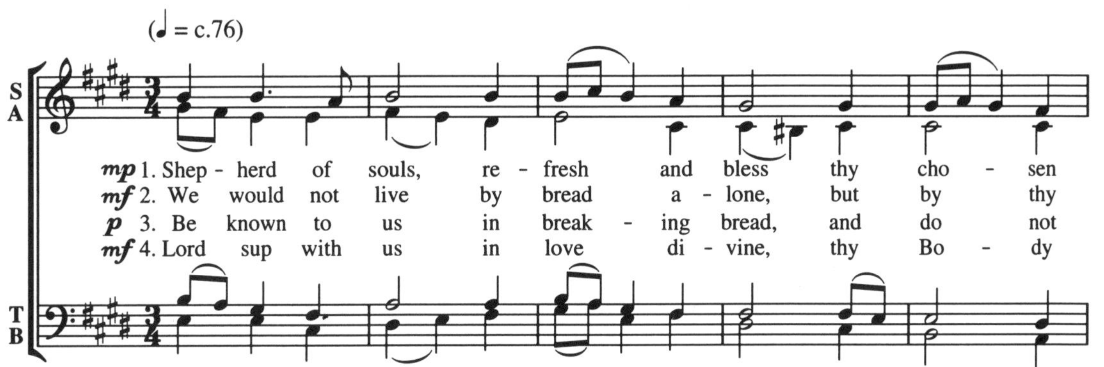

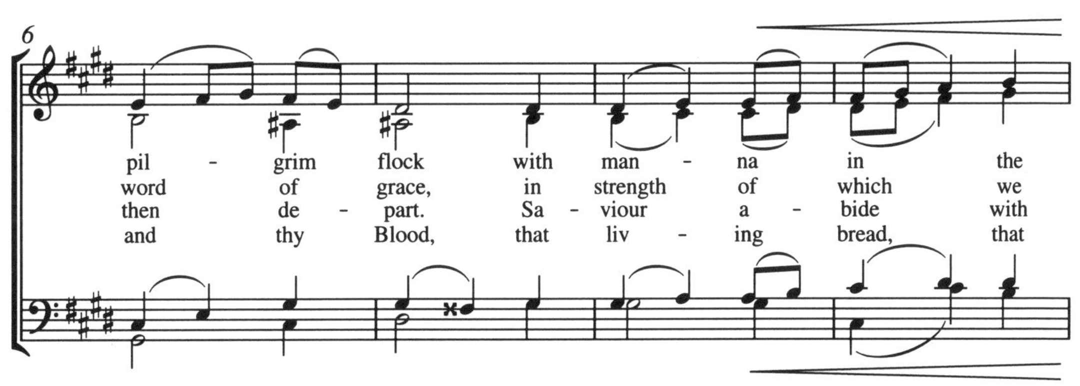

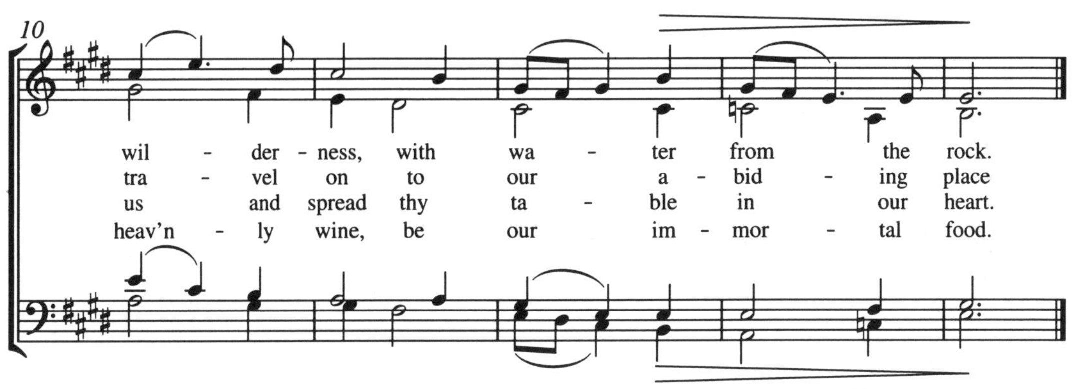

For John and Pamela Edmonds

I WILL LIFT UP MINE EYES

Text: from Psalm 121
Music: Alan Ridout (1934-1996)

13
self is thy keep - er, the Lord is thy de -

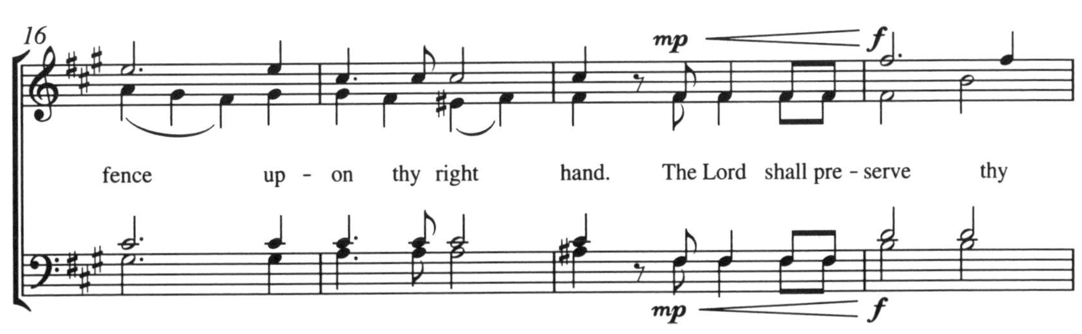
16
mp
f
fence up - on thy right hand. The Lord shall pre - serve thy
mp
f

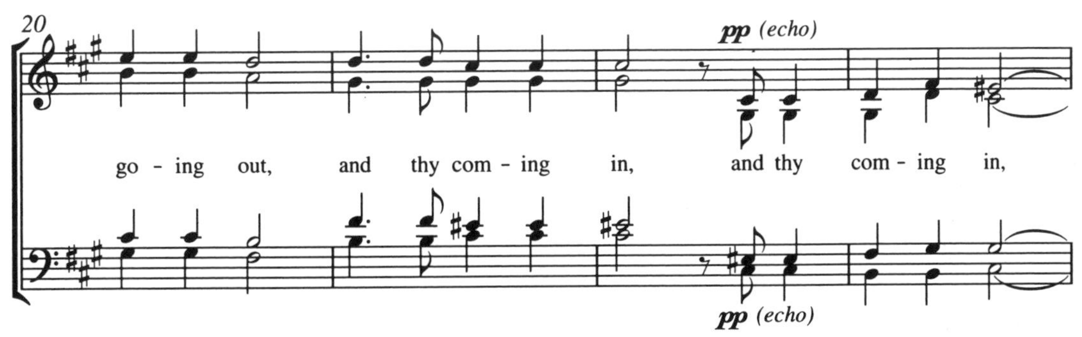
20
pp (echo)
go - ing out, and thy com - ing in, and thy com - ing in,
pp (echo)

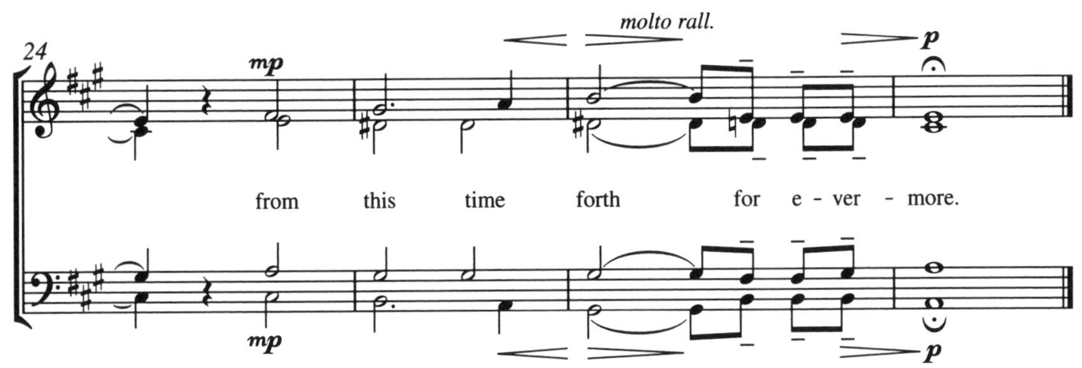
24
molto rall.
mp
p
from this time forth for e - ver - more.
mp
p

SPIRIT OF GOD

Text: Cecil Alexander (1818-1895)
Music: David Terry (b.1975)

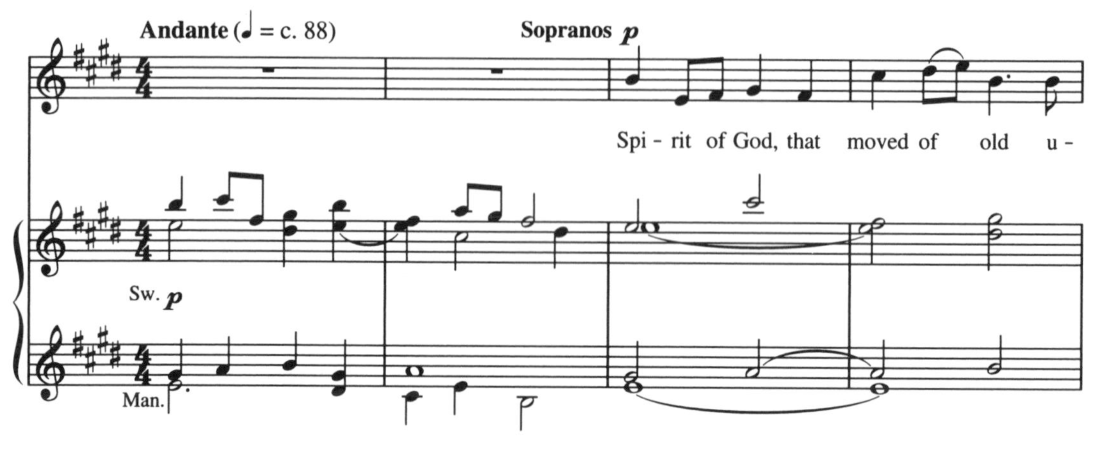

13
mf
S
A
Thou that art pow'r and peace com - bined, all high-est strength, all
T
B
mf
16
cresc.
f
dim.
pur - est love, the rush-ing of the migh - ty wind, the brood-ing of the
cresc.
dim.
f
20
p
mf cresc.
unis.
gen - tle dove, come, give us still thy pow'r-ful aid, and urge us on, and
unis.
p
mf cresc.
Gt. mf
cresc.

24
f
keep us thine; nor leave the hearts that once were made fit tem-ples for thy
f
f
28
sempre f
grace di - vine; nor let us quench thy sev'n - fold light; but
sempre f
sempre f
31
div.
cresc.
still with soft - est breath - ings stir our way - ward souls, and
cresc.
cresc.

34
A - - - men.
ff
poco rit.
ff
lead us right, O Ho - ly Ghost, the com - for - ter.
ff
poco rit.
ff

O SAVING VICTIM

Text: attr. Thomas Aquinas (1227-1274), trans. Edward Caswall (1814-1878)
Music: Stanley Vann (b.1910)

HOLY, HOLY, HOLY

Text: Translated from the German by Christina Cumming Cairns
Music: Franz Schubert (1797-1828)

BE STILL, FOR THE PRESENCE OF THE LORD

Text: David J. Evans (b.1957)
Music: David J. Evans, arr. Christopher Tambling

10
Unison
In him no
No work too
fore him now with re - ve - rence and fear.
cleanse and heal, to mi - ni - ster his grace.
14
sin is found, we stand on ho - ly ground. Be still, for the
hard for him, in faith re - ceive from him. Be still, for the
18
(v. 3 rit.)
Fine
pre - sence of the Lord, the Ho - ly One, is here.
pow - er of the Lord is mov - ing in this place.
(v. 3 rit.)
Fine

21
v.2 unaccompanied
f
S
A
shi - ning all a -
2. Be still, for the glo - ry of the Lord is shi - ning all a -
T
B
f

24
round,
round, is shi - ning round; he burns with ho - ly fire, with

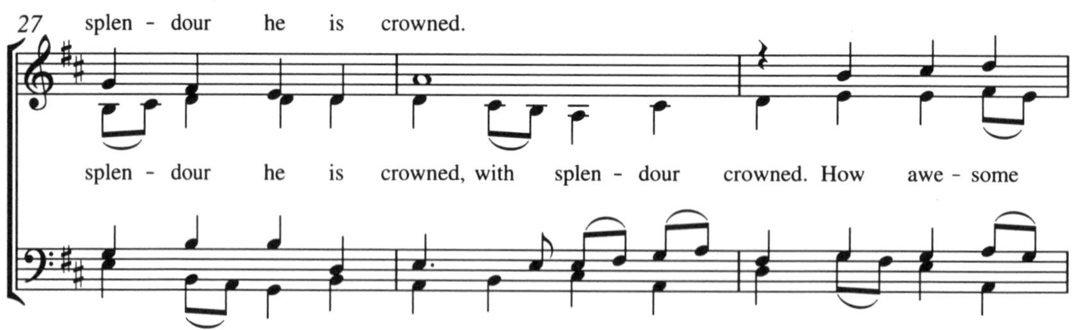
27
splen - dour he is crowned.
splen - dour he is crowned, with splen - dour crowned. How awe - some

30
is the sight, our ra - diant King of light!
is the sight, our ra - diant King, our King of, King of

33
light! Be still, for the glo - ry of the Lord is

35
D.S. al Fine
shi - ning all a - round.
D.S. al Fine

SPIRIT OF GOD

Text: Michael Forster (b.1946)
Music: Charles Gounod (1818-1893)
adapted and arranged by Alan Ridout

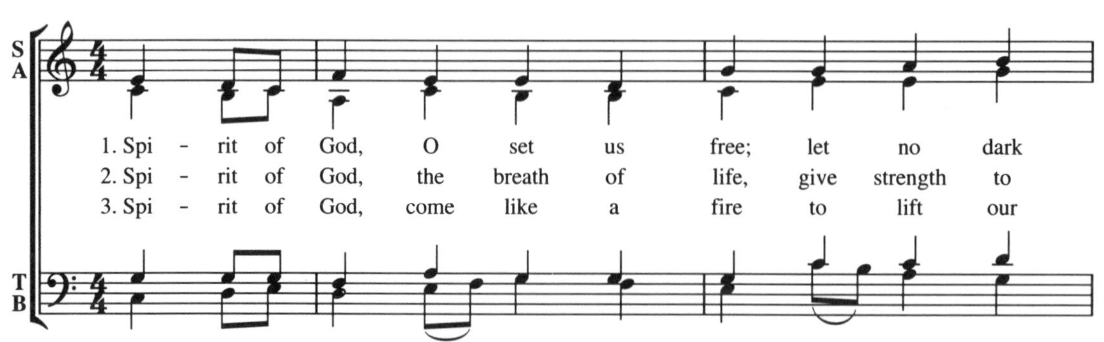

9
vine. We long to see, to touch, to know, and fear the
sire. You call us on to life and hope from all that
light. And when, with mem - 'ry's dis - tant view, we long for

12
risk that faith de - mands; O help us tread the de - sert
would our souls en - slave; O may our faith - less hearts not
some en - chan - ted past, then give us grace to fol - low

15
road that leads us to the pro - mised land.
choose the spu - rious safe - ty of the grave.
him who is the on - ly first and last.

THE LORD'S PRAYER

Text: The Gospels
Music: Martin Setchell (b.1949)

f
we for-give those who sin a-gainst us. Lead us not in-to temp-
f

p
mf
ta - tion, but de - li - ver us from e - vil. For the
p
mf

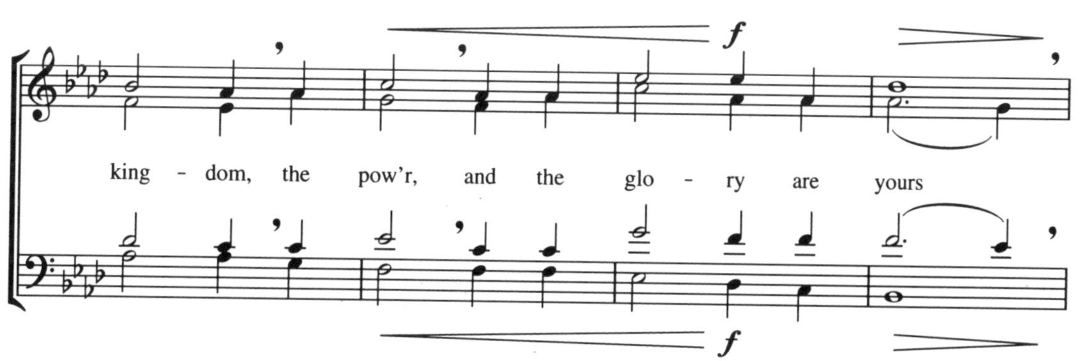
f
king - dom, the pow'r, and the glo - ry are yours
f

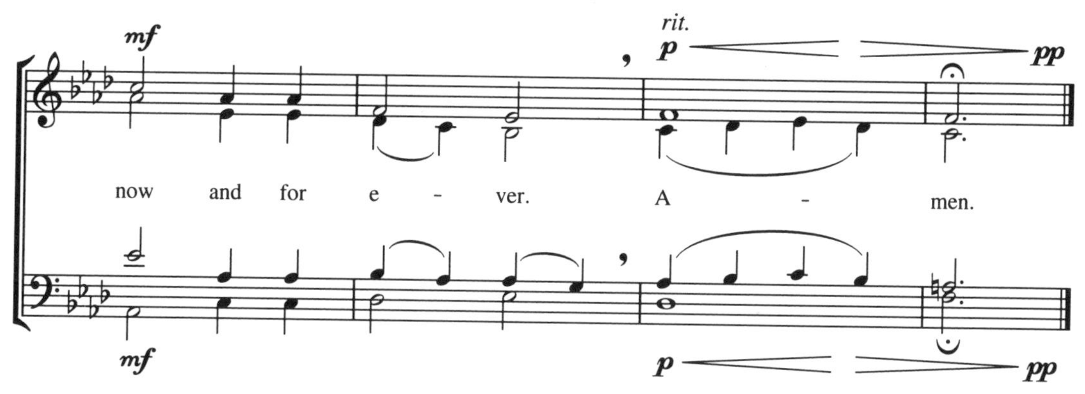
mf
rit.
p
pp
now and for e - ver. A - men.
mf
p
pp